Kate's Book

Unit 5 Reader

Skills Strand

GRADE 1

Amplify learning.

Core Knowledge®

Table of Contents
Kate's Book
Unit 5 Reader

A Letter from Kate 1

In the Cave 2

The Coin Shop. 8

You Never Can Tell. 14

The Offer 20

The Campsite 22

Jack's Tale 26

The Visit 32

The Hike 38

The Bone Man 46

Two Good Things and One Bad Thing 52

The Big Dig 56

The Scoop 62

Pausing Point (Stories for Assessment and Enrichment)

We Are TV Stars 70

Nan's Book 74

The Book Shop 78

We Make a Book 82

A Lett·er from Kate

I'm Kate Skipp·er, and this is my book!

This book tells what I did last summ·er when I was nine. My mom and dad took me to vis·it with my Nan. Nan is my mom's mom. She is an art·ist, and she has a cab·in out in the West.

At the start of my time with Nan, I was sad. It seemed like it would be a bor·ing summ·er. But in the end I had a lot of fun.

I made this book to tell you all the fun stuff I did last summ·er. When I fin·ished it, Nan made the art. You have the book we made in your hands.
I hope you like it!

Kate Skipper

ME ₊ NAN!

1

In the Cave

When I went to vis·it with Nan, I was sad. I missed Mom and Dad. But Nan cheered me up and made things fun.

Nan took me on hikes. The land I saw in the West was not at all like the land I am used to. <u>Where</u> I am from, things are green in the summ·er, and there are lots of trees. Out in the West, there are hills and red rocks, but not a lot of trees. In s<u>ome</u> spots, you can hike for a mile and not see one tree!

<u>Once</u>, Nan and I were on a hike when it start·ed to storm. Nan and I went in·to a cave so that we would not get wet.

As we were stand·ing there, I saw some·thing shimm·er in the dark.

"Nan," I said, point·ing at the spot, "what's that?"

"Well," said Nan, "let's have a look."

We looked and saw some·thing stuck in a crack in the rock. I grabbed it.

"It's a coin!" I said.

"Well, I'll be!" said Nan.

I said, "What sort of coin is it?"

Nan said, "I can't tell. It looks like it could be made of sil·ver."

Then she said, "I have a pal, Jack, who is an ex·pert on coins. We can bring it to him to·morr·ow, and he will tell us what sort of coin it is."

I dropped the coin in my pock·et, and we went on with our hike.

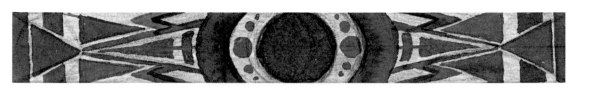

The Coin Shop

Nan drove us to the coin shop.

The man in the coin shop was a pal of hers. His name was Jack.

"Jack," Nan said, "this is Kate Skipp·er. I'm Kate's nan. She's out here for the summ·er. We went for a hike, and Kate found a coin in a cave."

"Well, Miss Skipp·er," Jack said, "let's have a look at it!"

I hand·ed him the coin.

Jack set it un·der a look·ing glass and swi**tch**ed on a lamp. "Let's see," he said. "It's got some scra**tch**·es on it. But I can tell that it's a Span·ish coin. It's made of sil·ver, too."

9

"When was it made?" asked Nan.

"There's n<u>o</u> date on the coin," said Jack. "But I'll bet it dates back to the six·teen hun·dreds. The Span·ish mint·ed a big ba**tch** of coins like this one back then."

"Good·ness!" said Nan.

"Is that a long time back in the past?" I asked.

"Yes," said Jack. "Let me run and fe**tch** my book on Span·ish coins."

When Jack came back, he said, "There's just one thing I need you to tell me, Miss Skipp·er."

"What's that?" I asked.

"Are there a lot of coins like this one in that cave?"

"No," I said, "we found just this one."

"That's a shame," Jack said.

"Why?" I asked.

"If there were a lot of coins, you and your Nan would be rich!" said Jack. "I could sell a coin like this for three hun·dred bucks!"

"Three hun·dred bucks?" said Nan.

Jack nodd·ed.

"Yipp·ee!" I shout·ed. "I'm rich!"

You Never Can Tell

Jack said that he c<u>ou</u>ld sell the coin that I found for three hun·dred bucks. But I kept it and took it back to Nan's cab·in.

We got a snack from the ki**tch**·en and then start·ed to chat.

"Can I see the coin?" Nan asked.

I stre**tch**ed out my arm and gave it to her.

"If this coin had lips," Nan said, "what would it tell us? Would it tell us <u>who</u> left it in that cave and <u>why</u> he or she was there? What ma**g**·ic tale could it tell us?"

"I wish it would," I said. "What is the le**g**·end of this coin?

I stared at the coin for a bit.

"C<u>ou</u>ld it be that a robb·er hid it there?" I asked. "Did they have robb·ers back then?"

"You bet they did," said Nan. "But <u>why</u> would the robb·er hide just one coin? It seems like he would hide a lar**ge** ba**tch** of coins."

"Per·haps he did not have a lar**ge** ba**tch**," I said. "Per·haps this was all he stole."

"If that's all he stole," said Nan, "then he was not such a good robb·er!"

"Nan," I said, "there's no such thing as a good robb·er!"

Nan smiled and nodd·ed.

Af·ter a bit I said, "If this coin costs three hun·dred bucks, a robb·er would feel like he had to hide it."

"Well," Nan said. "Span·ish coins like this one are rare, so Jack can sell them for a lot of cash. But back when this coin was made, it was not rare. There were a lot of coins just like this one. Back then this coin was sort of like a dime."

I took a dime out of my pock·et and said, "So if I keep this dime for a long time, un·til it gets rare and there are not a lot of them left, will it be a three hun·dred buck dime?"

"It could happ·en," said Nan. "You nev·er can tell!"

The Offer

I was sitt·ing in the ki**tch**·en, scra**tch**·ing a lar**ge** bug bite on my leg, when Nan came in.

"I just spoke with Jack," she said. "He made us an off·er."

"What sort of off·er?"

"He off·ered to take us camp·ing with him and Max."

"Who is Max?"

"Max is nine, like you. Jack is his grand·dad."

"What would we do?" I asked.

"Well, we would hike, look at rocks, cook lunch and dinn·er out·side, look at the stars, and sleep in a tent."

"**G**ee," I said, "that sounds like fun! When can we start?"

"To·morr·ow morn·ing!" Nan said.

The Campsite

Jack came and picked us up in his truck. We drove to a camp·site in the Bad·lands.

"Nan," I said, "what's up with that name—the Bad·lands?"

"Well," said Nan, "leg·end has it that a long time back, farm·ers came out here look·ing for farm·land. When they saw all of the rocks and sand and stone, they said, 'This is bad land! We can't plant crops here!' And the name Bad·lands just sort of stuck."

"It's bad land for farm·ing," said Jack. "But it's good land for camp·ing!"

When we got to the camp·site, we had to un·pack sleep·ing bags, tents, lan·terns, ma**tch**·es, and lots of food. We lugged it all to the camp·site.

Jack chose a spot to set up camp. Max and I helped set up the tents. It took us a long time.

For dinn·er we had hot dogs. We stuck them on sticks and held them in the fire. My hot dog got all black b<u>e</u>·c<u>au</u>se I left it in there too long. Max gave me one of his.

That was when I said to my·self, "Max is OK!"

Jack's Tale

Af·ter dinn·er we munched on some gin·ger snaps. Then Jack shared an out·law tale.

"This happ·ened out here in the West a long time back," said Jack, "in an age when there were no cars and no planes. Back then, if you had to send a lett·er, you sent it by stage·coach."

"The stage·coach was sort of like a car, but it was drawn by hors·es. There was a place where men could sit in·side. But the man who drove the stage·coach sat out·side up on top."

"The man <u>who</u> drove the stage·coach kept the strong·box next to him. The strong·box was a locked box <u>where</u> he kept the cash."

"Some·times out·laws would rob the stage·coach. Those out·laws were bad men. But there was one <u>who</u> some said was a bit bett·er than the rest. His name was Bart."

"Bart was a sharp dress·er. He did his robb·ing in a jack·et and a black top hat. He had the best mann·ers you ev·er saw. When he robbed, he did not yell and shout at the men he was robb·ing. Not Bart! He tipped his hat."

"Then he said, 'Ex·cuse me, **g**ents. Would you be so fine as to pass d<u>ow</u>n the strong·box with the cash in it?'"

"No!" said Nan.

"Yes!" said Jack. "It's not just a le**g**·end. It's a fact. You can look it up!"

"Did they catch him?" Max asked.

"Nope," said Jack, "he came back and robbed the stage·c<u>oa</u>ch lots of times."

"Did they ev·er ca**tch** him?" I asked.

"Yes, af·ter a long hunt, they nabbed him. They char**ge**d him with theft and locked him up for a long time. He did his time. Then they let him back out."

"Then what happ·ened?" I asked.

Jack said, "Bart shaped up in the
end. When they let him out, he said he
was fin·ished with crime."

"That's cool!" said Max.

The Visit

Af·ter tell·ing us the tale, Jack said, "It's time to pack up the food."

We stuffed the food in·to a lar**ge** pack with a rope on it. Jack tossed the rope up in·to a tree and hoist·ed the food pack up so that it was hang·ing ten feet off of the ground.

"Paw-paw," said Max, "why do we have to keep the food up in the tree?"

"Be·cause it will keep the food safe from fox·es and racc·oons that would like to snack on it," Jack said.

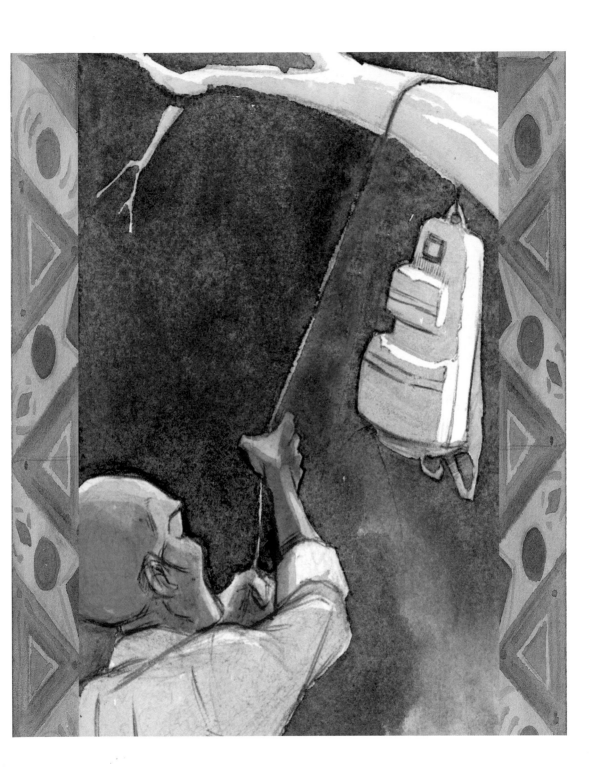

Af·ter that, we crawled in·to the tents, flipped off our lan·terns, and went to sleep.

Nan and I slept well un·til a loud clatt·er out·side woke us up.

"What was that?" I asked.

"I can't tell," said Nan, as she hugged me close to her.

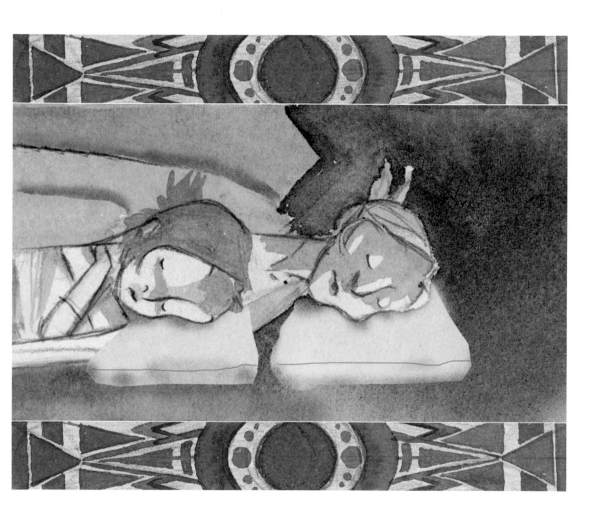

Jack ran out·side with his lan·tern and yelled, "Get out of here! Scram! Get lost!"

When we went out, we saw Jack and Max stand·ing there. Jack had his lan·tern.

"Jack," Nan asked, "who came to vis·it?"

"I did not see it," said Jack, "but I'm bett·ing it was a fox who was look·ing for some scraps of food. He bumped in·to the pots and pans. The clatt·er of the pots and pans must have scared him off."

"Is that why we hoist·ed the food pack up in the tree?" Max asked.

"That's why!" said Jack.

The Hike

The next morn·ing, we went on a hike. Af·ter a bit, we stopped for lunch.

When Max fin·ished his lunch, he asked, "Can Kate and I look for rocks?"

Jack said OK.

"Kate," Max said to me, "bring your fork. We can use it to dig up rocks."

I grabbed my fork, and we went off to look for rocks.

Max point·ed at a bump on the side of a cliff and said, "Let's dig that rock out!"

The rock did not look all that lar**ge**. But when we start·ed digg·ing, we soon saw that it was lar**g**·er than it had seemed.

Af·ter a bit, Max said, "**G**ee! It must be <u>two</u> feet long! We need to keep scra**tch**·ing in or·der to car**ve** it out of the side of the cliff."

We went on scra**tch**·ing with our forks.

"Let's tug on it!" Max said. "I bet we can get it out b<u>y</u> our·sel**ve**s."

We grabbed and tugged it.

It popped out. But so did a big cloud of sand and dust. Max and I fell d<u>ow</u>n.

<u>Once</u> the dust and sand had drift·ed off, I saw Max stand·ing there with the thing in his hands.

"It's not a rock!" he yelled. "It's a bone!"

It was the bigg·est bone I had ev·er seen. It was three feet long!

Jack and Nan came runn·ing.

"Good·ness!" said Nan. "That is one large bone! <u>Where</u> did you get it?"

Max point·ed to the spot <u>where</u> we found it.

Jack set the bone on the ground. Then he took a pic·<u>ture</u> of the bone and said, "We need to get an ex·pert to look at this bone and tell us what sort of bone it is."

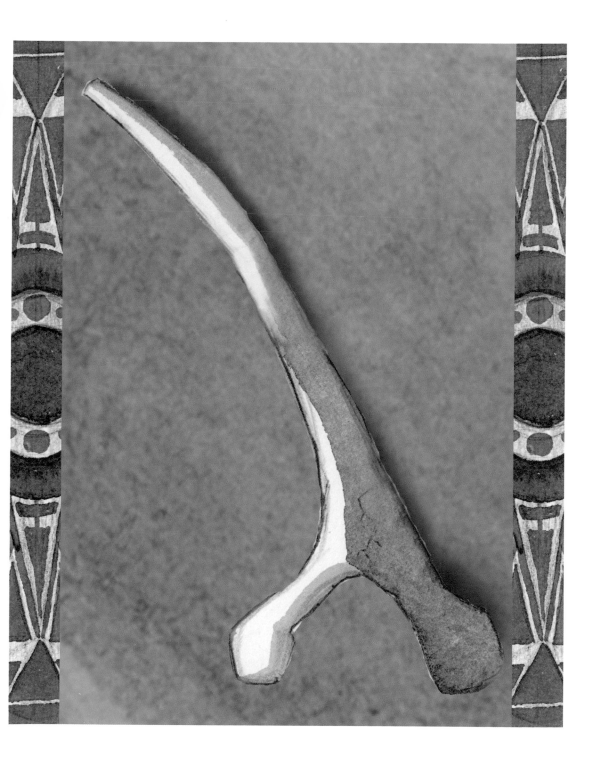

The Bone Man

The next morn·ing, Jack said, "I just had a chat with a man from West·ern State Coll·e**ge**. His name is Ron Fi**tch**, and he is an ex·pert on bones. He has **wr**itt·en lots of books. If we bring him the bone, he can tell us what sort of bone it is."

"He's a bone man?" asked Max.

"Yep," said Jack.

We got in·to the truck. Jack said that I was in char**ge** of the bone. I **wr**apped it up and set it on my lap.

When we got to the coll·e**ge**, we gave the bone man the bone. When he saw it, he broke in·to a big grin.

The bone man bent d<u>ow</u>n and said, "I could be **wr**ong, but it looks like you**'ve** found some·thing big here! I have to do some tests, but I'll bet this is a bone of a T. rex."

"Sweet!" yelled Max.

"What's a T. rex?" I asked.

Max looked at me like I was from Mars.

"Kate!" he said, "T. rex is like the cool·est, bigg·est rep·tile of all time!"

The bone man went and got a book. He point·ed to a lar**ge** pic·<u>ture</u> of a T. rex.

49

"Jeep·ers," I said, "he *is* big! <u>Why</u> have I nev·er seen a T. rex like this at the zoo?"

The bone man smiled. So did Nan and Jack.

"You can't see a T. rex at the zoo," the bone man said. "They were all wiped out a long time back in the past. The T. rex is ex·tinct. All that's left of them to·d<u>ay</u> are bones pres·er**ve**d in the ground. And there are not a lot of bones. That's <u>why</u> it's such a cool thing that you found this bone pres·er**ve**d in the side of the cliff!"

51

Two Good Things and One Bad Thing

The next week, Nan said, "I just spoke with Ron Fi**tch**, the bone man. I'**ve** got three things to tell you. T<u>wo</u> of them are good things that you will like. One is a bad thing that you will not like."

"Tell me one of the good things," I said.

"Mis·ter Fi**tch** got the tests back. The bone that you and Max found is a T. rex bone!"

"Yipp·ee!" I shout·ed. "I am glad that is sol**ve**d. Max will be so thrilled that he has a T. rex bone!"

"Well," said Nan, "that brings me to the bad thing."

"What is it?" I asked, scra**tch**·ing my **wr**ist.

"The bad thing is that you and Max will not get to keep the bone for your·sel**ve**s."

"<u>Why</u> not? Did we do some·thing **wr**ong?"

"Well," Nan said, "it's b<u>e</u>·c<u>au</u>se you found the bone in a state park. There is a law that says that you can't dig up bones in state parks and keep them for your·self."

"Bumm·er!" I said. "So who gets to keep it?"

"The state. Mis·ter Fi**tch** and his help·ers will keep the bone and dig up the rest of the bones, too. And that brings me to the last thing."

"This is a good thing?"

"Yes."

"Tell me!"

"They would like you and Max to vis·it them when they are digg·ing up the bones. And they would like the <u>two</u> of you to pick out a name for the T. rex that you found."

"Cool!" I said.

The Big Dig

When we went back to the cliff, the bone man was there with some help·ers. They had scraped the side of the cliff to ex·pose a lot of the T. rex.

"So, will you dig out all of the bones here on site?" asked Nan.

"No," said the bone man, "the next step will be to car**ve** this cliff in·to lar**ge** blocks of rock. Then we will **wr**ap the blocks up in plas·ter. The plas·ter will keep the bones from crack·ing. Then we will use a lar**ge** crane to set the blocks on trucks. Then the trucks will take them to my lab. <u>Once</u> the blocks are there, we will start digg·ing the bones out of the blocks."

"What sort of tools do you use for that?" asked Nan.

"We use tools a lot like the ones den·tists use on teeth—brush·es and sharp picks."

"Kate and I used forks!" said Max.

"How long will it take to car**ve** all of the bones out of the rocks?" Jack asked.

"Well," said the bone man, "we**'ve** got a lot to do. It will take some time be·cause we have to be care·ful not to **wr**eck the bones."

"Will you be fin·ished by the end of the summ·er?" I asked.

"No," said the bone man, "you and Max will have to vis·it next summ·er and per·haps the summ·er af·ter that. Then we can ca**tch** up on our digg·ing prog·ress!"

"So," said the bone man, "have you picked out a name for this T. rex?"

"Yes, I've picked one," I said.

All of the digg·ers stopped digg·ing and looked at me.

I said, "This T. rex will be named Max, or if you like, T. Max!"

All of the men cheered.

Max smiled.

The Scoop

Af·ter we named the T. rex, some men came char**g**·ing up to us.

"Can we shoot some film of you for TV?" one of them asked. "It would be a big scoop for us."

Nan and Jack said it was OK.

The men set up a bunch of stuff to shoot the film. Then one of them start·ed count·ing d<u>ow</u>n from ten. He said, "Three, t<u>wo</u>, one!" Then he point·ed at us.

The TV man spoke in·to a mike. He said, "This is Rog·er Fle**tch**·er. I'm stand·ing here in the Bad·lands, <u>where</u> t<u>wo</u> chil·dren have found the bones of a T. rex."

The man bent d<u>ow</u>n to Max and stuck the mike un·der his nose. He said, "What's y<u>our</u> name?"

Max looked like he was scared of the mike. He jumped back a bit. Then he mutt·ered, "I'm Max."

"And you?"

I said, "I'm Kate." Then I waved.

"Max," said the man, "<u>where</u> did you spot the bone?"

Max said, "It was stick·ing out of the side of a cliff."

67

"Kate, could you tell it was a bone when you saw it?"

"No," I said, "it looked like a rock."

"What did you use to dig it out?"

"We used our forks!" said Max.

"Forks!" said the man. "That's cool. Could I get a close-up of the t<u>wo</u> of you with y<u>our</u> forks?"

Some·one ran and got us t<u>wo</u> forks. We held them up and smiled un·til the man said, "Cut!" And that was the end of that.

We Are TV Stars

We drove back to Nan's cab·in and got there just in time to see our·sel**ve**s on TV.

The TV man said, "This is Ro**g**·er Fle**tch**·er. I'm stand·ing here in the Bad·lands, where two children have found the bones of a T. rex."

Then Max and I saw our·sel**ve**s on TV.

"Woo-hoo!" I shout·ed. "We are TV. stars!"

Then came the part where the TV. man asked Max his name, and Max looked like he was scared of the mike.

"Max, you goof!" I said. "Why did you jump back like that?"

Max just shrugged.

Next the TV man asked me my name.

I said, "I'm Kate." Then I waved.

"Max," said the TV man, "<u>where</u> did you spot the bone?"

Max said, "It was stick·ing out of the side of a cliff."

"What did you use to dig it out?"

"We used our forks!" said Max.

Then we saw the close-up of Max and me with our forks.

"So there you have it!" said the TV man. "I'm Rog·er Fle**tch**·er with a tale of two chil·dren, two forks, and one lar**ge** T. rex!"

Nan's Book

Max and I and the T. rex were on TV six times. I was glad when it came to an end. Af·ter you smile and wave a fork six times, it gets to be less fun.

One morn·ing, Nan hand·ed me a book and said, "Let's drive to the book shop."

"Nan," I said, "why do you need to get a book at the book shop when you have this one?"

"I just fin·ished that one," Nan said. "I liked it a lot. And it just so happ·ens that the man who **wr**ote it will be at the book shop to·d<u>ay</u>. I'd like to meet him."

In the car I looked at the book. It said "Dust Up, by Stan Bend·er."

"What sort of book is this?" I asked.

"It's a west·ern," said Nan.

"What's a west·ern?"

"It's a book set out here in the West."

"Is there an out·law in the book like Bart?"

"There's an out·law," said Nan, "but he's not like Bart."

"Why not?"

"He has bad mann·ers!" said Nan.

I looked at the last page and saw the page num·ber: 305.

"Yikes!" I said. "This is a long book!"

"It is," said Nan. "But it felt short to me be·cause I liked it so much. I was sad when I got to the end!"

I start·ed to look in·side the book, but just then Nan said, "Here we are!"

The Book Shop

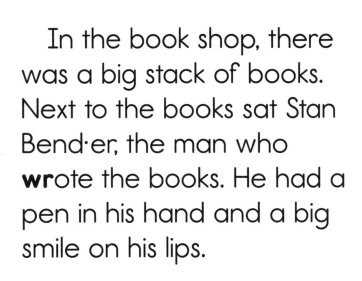

In the book shop, there was a big stack of books. Next to the books sat Stan Bend·er, the man who **wr**ote the books. He had a pen in his hand and a big smile on his lips.

"You'd smile too if your book were sell·ing as well as his is!" Nan said.

Nan and I went and stood in line to meet Stan Bend·er.

Nan shook hands with him and said, "I've got twelve of your books. This one was your best book yet!"

The man smiled and said, "That's sweet of you! I hope you will pick up my next one, too!"

"I will!" said Nan.

Then the man wrote, "Best wish·es, Stan Bend·er," in Nan's book.

"Mis·ter Bend·er," I asked, "how hard was it to write that book?"

"Well," he said, "this one was not all that hard. The last one I did was a lot hard·er."

As we got back in the car, I said, "Nan, I'd like to write a book."

"What sort of book would it be?" Nan asked.

"Well," I said, "Max and I found the T. rex."

"Yes, you did," said Nan.

"And you and I found that coin."

"Yes," said Nan.

"And we are out here in the West."

"Yes."

"So it could be a bones and coins and west·ern sort of book."

"Why not?" said Nan. "If you **wr**ite it, I will make the pic·<u>tures</u>."

I said, "Shake on it!" Then we shook hands.

We Make a Book

When we got back to Nan's, I start·ed to **wr**ite the book. I **wr**ote down all of the cool stuff that happ·ened to me out West. The hard·est part was gett·ing start·ed. Once I got started, it went fast.

Nan helped me pick out good words. Some·times when you **wr**ite, you have to **wr**ite things two or three times to get all of the best words and get them in the best or·der.

Max helped me out, too. He said, "I can help you with spell·ing. I am the best spell·er in my class." Max looked at what I had **wr**itt·en and fixed a lot of spell·ing mis·takes that I had made.

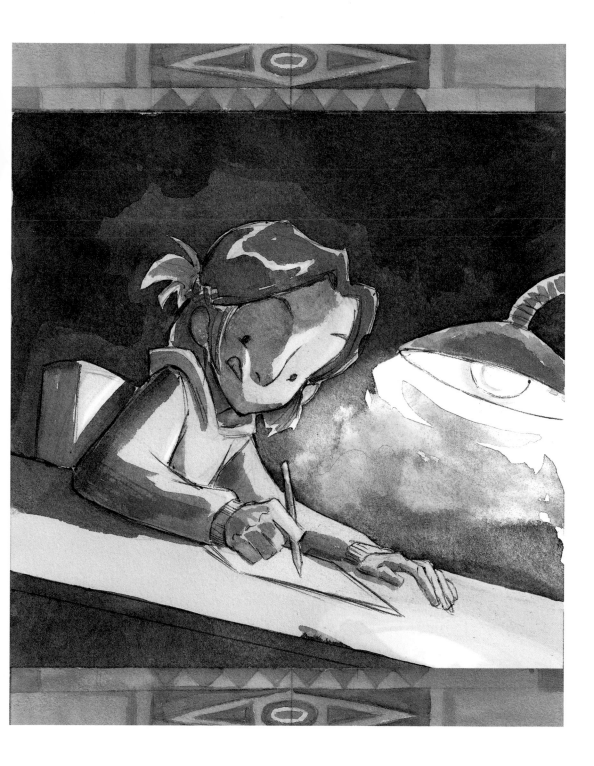

When I had **wr**itt·en the words, Nan got out her brush and start·ed to make the art. It took her a long time. She sent the pic·<u>tures</u> to me three weeks af·ter I went home.

My dad took me and my book to a pal of his to see if he would pub·lish the book.

The man looked at it and said, "This is well-**wr**itt·en! Chil·dren out there will like this book. I'd like to print it!"

I was so glad, I shout·ed, "Yipp·ee!"

The man and his staff got the book all set to pub·lish. Then they sent it to a print·er.

I hope you liked the book.

If you'd like to **wr**ite me a lett·er, you can send it to me at this add·ress:

Kate Skipper

c/o Core Knowledge Foundation

801 East High Street

Charlottesville, Virginia 22902

Core Knowledge Language Arts

Series Editor-in-Chief
E. D. Hirsch, Jr.

President
Linda Bevilacqua

Editorial Staff
Carolyn Gosse, Senior Editor - Preschool
Khara Turnbull, Materials Development Manager
Michelle L. Warner, Senior Editor - Listening & Learning

Mick Anderson
Robin Blackshire
Maggie Buchanan
Paula Coyner
Sue Fulton
Sara Hunt
Erin Kist
Robin Luecke
Rosie McCormick
Cynthia Peng
Liz Pettit
Ellen Sadler
Deborah Samley
Diane Auger Smith
Sarah Zelinke

Design and Graphics Staff
Scott Ritchie, Creative Director

Kim Berrall
Michael Donegan
Liza Greene
Matt Leech
Bridget Moriarty
Lauren Pack

Consulting Project Management Services
ScribeConcepts.com

Additional Consulting Services
Ang Blanchette
Dorrit Green
Carolyn Pinkerton

Acknowledgments
These materials are the result of the work, advice, and encouragement of numerous individuals over many years. Some of those singled out here already know the depth of our gratitude; others may be surprised to find themselves thanked publicly for help they gave quietly and generously for the sake of the enterprise alone. To helpers named and unnamed we are deeply grateful.

Contributors to Earlier Versions of these Materials
Susan B. Albaugh, Kazuko Ashizawa, Nancy Braier, Kathryn M. Cummings, Michelle De Groot, Diana Espinal, Mary E. Forbes, Michael L. Ford, Ted Hirsch, Danielle Knecht, James K. Lee, Diane Henry Leipzig, Martha G. Mack, Liana Mahoney, Isabel McLean, Steve Morrison, Juliane K. Munson, Elizabeth B. Rasmussen, Laura Tortorelli, Rachael L. Shaw, Sivan B. Sherman, Miriam E. Vidaver, Catherine S. Whittington, Jeannette A. Williams

We would like to extend special recognition to Program Directors Matthew Davis and Souzanne Wright who were instrumental to the early development of this program.

Schools
We are truly grateful to the teachers, students, and administrators of the following schools for their willingness to field test these materials and for their invaluable advice: Capitol View Elementary, Challenge Foundation Academy (IN), Community Academy Public Charter School, Lake Lure Classical Academy, Lepanto Elementary School, New Holland Core Knowledge Academy, Paramount School of Excellence, Pioneer Challenge Foundation Academy, New York City PS 26R (The Carteret School), PS 30X (Wilton School), PS 50X (Clara Barton School), PS 96Q, PS 102X (Joseph O. Loretan), PS 104Q (The Bays Water), PS 214K (Michael Friedsam), PS 223Q (Lyndon B. Johnson School), PS 308K (Clara Cardwell), PS 333Q (Goldie Maple Academy), Sequoyah Elementary School, South Shore Charter Public School, Spartanburg Charter School, Steed Elementary School, Thomas Jefferson Classical Academy, Three Oaks Elementary, West Manor Elementary.

And a special thanks to the CKLA Pilot Coordinators Anita Henderson, Yasmin Lugo-Hernandez, and Susan Smith, whose suggestions and day-to-day support to teachers using these materials in their classrooms was critical.